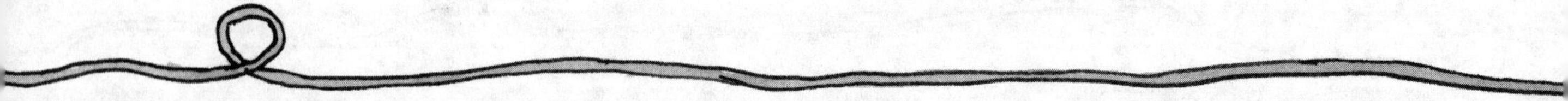

SO MANY DYNAMOS!

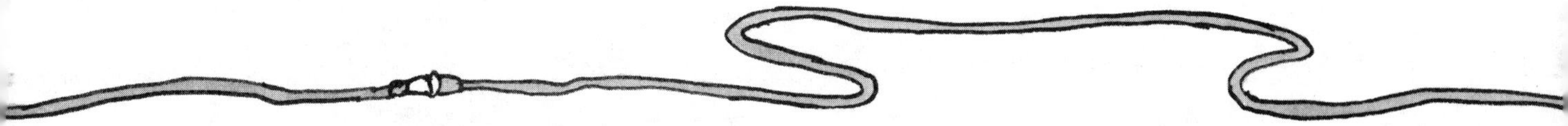

SO

MANY DYNAMOS!

and Other Palindromes

by JON AGEE

A Sunburst Book

Farrar · Straus · Giroux

To Dan Feigelson

Library of Congress catalog card number: 94-73749
Published in Canada by HarperCollins*CanadaLtd*
Printed and bound in the United States of America
Reprinted by arrangement with Farrar, Straus & Giroux.
10 9 8 7 6 5 4 3 2 1

TODD ERASES
A RED DOT

PORCH CROP

NO DRESSER,
DON ?

BORROW OR ROB?

NATE BIT
A TIBETAN

MASSIVE LEVI'S, SAM!

PUPIL'S SLIPUP

Cafe Facade
ED, A CAFE FACADE!
Menu

STIFF FITS

WAS IT A RAT I SAW?
CHEESE
CHEESE
CHEESE

USA
USA
rocket booster
Football
Lunar mitten
polka-dotted tie
new space-suit
autograph
fishing pole
space helmet
Sport jacket
golf clubs
calculator
new lunar boots

A SANTA AT NASA

WON'T I PANIC IN A PIT NOW?

DIANA BRUNO, ON URBAN AID

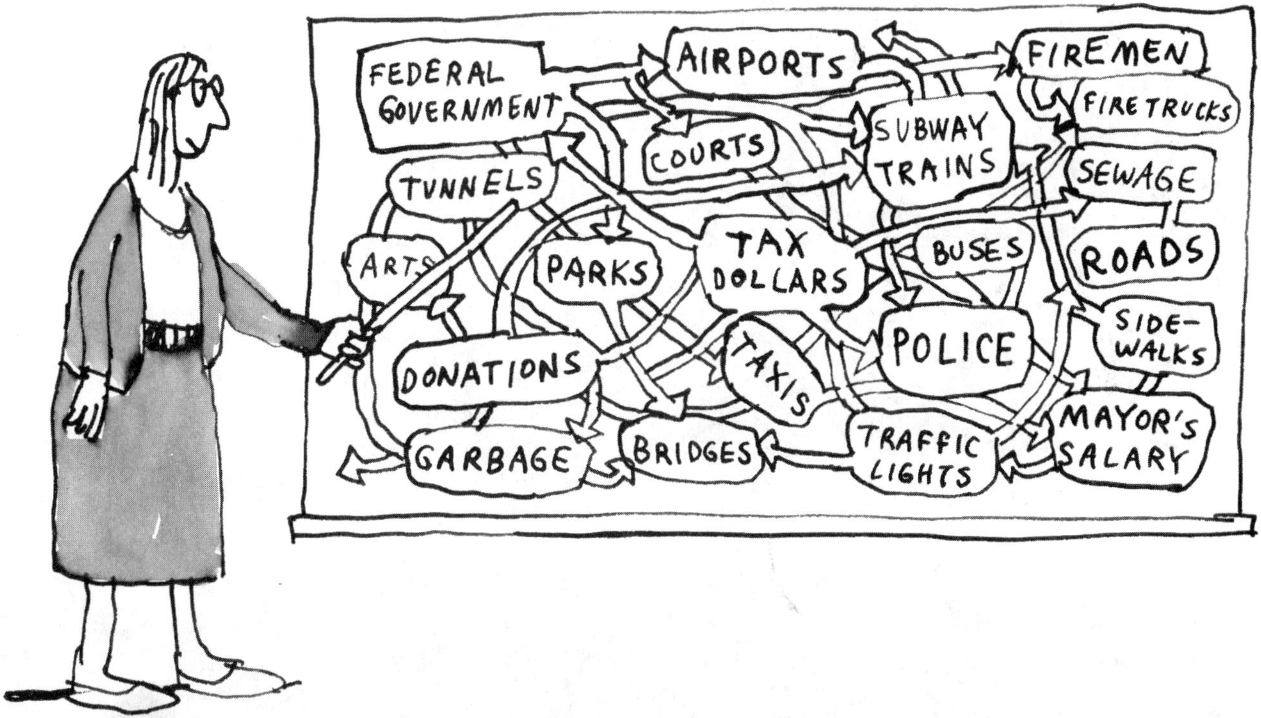

OTTO MADE
NED A MOTTO

LIAR
TRAIL

SON,
I SACK
CASINOS

CASINO
FRANKIE SLOTS
AND THE IRV
CAHILL ORCHESTRA
MARCH 20 & 21
HIGH ROLLER LOUNGE
LITTLE JOES SALOON
BULLSEYE

DALI
LAD

ED IS BUSY!
SUBSIDE!
ABC
CNN
TV
CBS
NBC
PBS

RON... I'M A MINOR!

TUBE DEBUT

1st Annual Bone-Tasting Contest
1
2
3

TOO BAD
I HID A
BOOT

RATS PARADED A RAP STAR

EVADE ME, DAVE!

WEE LUNAR GRANULE! EW!

STRAW WARTS

CORN AND NUTS CEREAL
MILLET
NUTRI-
MUESLI
BRAN
TRUE BRAN
ORTHO GRAIN
RYE FLAKES
CORN MASH
TOASTED ORGANIC MILLET CHIPS
SKIM MILK

GRANOLA SALON? ARG!
OATS N BERRIES
BRAN FLAKES
SKIM MILK
OATS
Muesli
CRUNCHY MILLET FLAKES
MUESLI
SKIM MILK
TOASTED WHEAT CHIPS
99

AMORAL
AROMA

SPOON IT IN...
...OOPS!

AS I PEE, SIR, I SEE PISA!

DR. AWKWARD
216
217
215
214
201

REMARKABLE MELBA KRAMER

Melba
MELBA
Melba
go melba
Melba

AN IGLOO-POOL, GINA!

MAO
FOAM

TIN SANITARY RAT, IN A SNIT

WANT SERENE REST?
NAW

SIT ON A POTATO PAN, OTIS!
CINEFLEX
"WORLD WITHOUT CHAIRS"
TAKE 13
Rector

FLO, GIN IS A SIN! I GOLF!

TOO FAR AFOOT

TEN ALPS
BORDERED
ROB'S PLANET

SEWER EWES

NO, SIR! AWAY! A PAPAYA WAR IS ON!
JUANITA'S FRUIT

PEDRO'S
FRUIT

DAD'S DAD'S
DAD

AN ERROR, RENA!

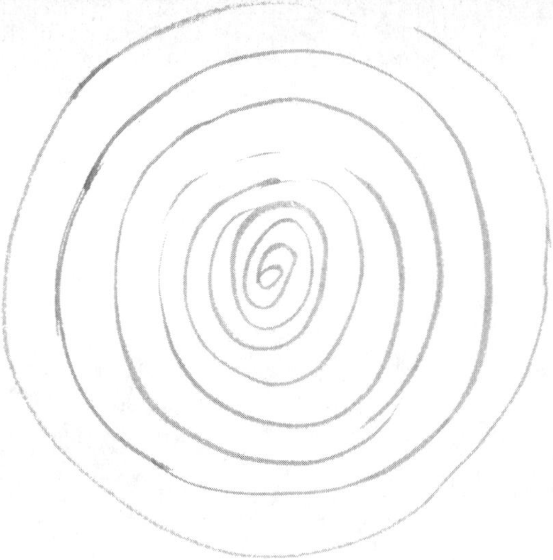

TOO HOT
TO HOOT

GABE'S ON A NOSEBAG

MAD AT ADAM?

SNOT OR PROTONS?

EMU FUME

A SLEEVE, ELSA
sleeves
sleeves
sleeves

"NO"'S IN UNISON

NO! PUT EGG GETUP ON!

HAPPY
EASTER

RED RUM, SIR, IS MURDER!

BOREDOM
ALA MODE,
ROB?
ICE CREAM
ROB

SWAP FOR A JAR OF PAWS?
HEADS
PAWS
TAILS
EARS
LEGS

BOSTON
ODE: DO
NOT SOB
GO
RED SO
GO!
GAME
SIX OF
SERIES
TONITE!
NY

NOOSE?
SOON

Thanks to
Tom Bassmann, John Baumann, Dan Covino, Mel Hess, Yishane Lee, J. A. Lindon, and Gilly Youner for their palindromes, and to Henry Finkelstein and Melissa Mead for their contributions.

With apologies to Boston Red Sox fans

RED-ICE
CIDER
5¢ a cup

NO WORD, NO BOND, ROW ON